DADDY FELL INTO THE POND

DADDY FELL INTO THE POND

AND OTHER

POEMS FOR CHILDREN

BY ALFRED NOYES

ILLUSTRATIONS BY

FRITZ KREDEL

SHEED & WARD, INC.

NEW YORK : 1952

CONTENTS

PREFACE

Dear Children:

You are all probably under ninety; that is why I call you children.

I am writing this letter from a long way off, chiefly to tell you that Daddy really did fall into the pond, for of course you wouldn't want to read the book if he hadn't. There were big green waterlily leaves floating on the pond, and as he doesn't see very well just now, he thought the pond was a part of the lawn and walked straight into it. The splash was tremendous! His own children were delighted and asked him to do it again so that they might take a really good photograph of daddy looking pleasant—you know the kind—all his teeth showing in a beautiful smile. But he refused to do this because he thought it would frighten the ducks, who had already had the shock of their lives.

Many of the poems in this book were written to amuse my own children. Some of them were written in our island garden off the coast of England, and others on the coast of Maine where we spent two summers and had lots of adventures, of which I told in a book called The Secret of Pooduck Island. Pooduck was the Indian name for the place where the world ends; and the jolly part of it is that the place where the world ends is also the place where it begins.

ALFRED NOYES.

DADDY FELL INTO THE POND

DADDY FELL INTO THE POND

Everyone grumbled. The sky was grey.
We had nothing to do and nothing to say.
We were nearing the end of a dismal day,
And there seemed to be nothing beyond,
                    THEN
            Daddy fell into the pond!

And everyone's face grew merry and bright,
And Timothy danced for sheer delight.
"Give me the camera, quick, oh quick!
He's crawling out of the duckweed." *Click!*

Then the gardener suddenly slapped his knee,
And doubled up, shaking silently,
And the ducks all quacked as if they were daft,
And it sounded as if the old drake laughed.

O, there wasn't a thing that didn't respond
                    WHEN
            Daddy fell into the pond!

ME AND THE MOUSE

On winter days when the sky grows dark
And Nannie and I come in from the Park,
She hums to herself as we climb the stair
To the Nursery fire that is waiting there:
Nobody knows but Me and the Mouse
How cozy it is at the top of the house.

It's a bit of a secret, for (don't you see?)
I'm the Mouse and Nannie is *Me*,
And it's three flights up to the Nursery floor,
Where a little tin soldier guards the door.
Halt! Who goes there, at the top of the house,
But he clicks his heels for Me and the Mouse.

When it's really dark, and the storm wind blows,
Down in the drawing-room nobody knows
How, far above, at our Nursery tea,
The kettle can purr for Nannie and me:
Oh, nobody knows but Me and the Mouse
How cozy it is at the top of the house.

DRESSY DOCTOR DABBS

Dressy little Doctor Dabbs
Used to fish for soft-shelled crabs
With what appears extremely odd,
Hook and line and fishing-rod.
The man upon the pier said, "Dabbs,
Lines ain't used for catching crabs."
But Dabbs had read a little book
In which the crabber used a hook.
"Ask any fisherman you please,"
He said, "from Thames or Tyne or Tees.
Whether he catches trout or pike,
Or any other fish you like,
You'll find his hook is just like mine,
Fastened quite firmly to a line."

To this assertion Mrs. Dabbs
Could only faintly murmur, "Crabs?"
But all the children chorused, "Look!
It's quite a different kind of hook.
Look at the picture in the book.
The crab-hook there is three feet long,
A sort of poker with a prong."

He simply shook his silly head,
And would not hear a word they said.
The more they laughed, the more he tried
To dress up and look dignified.
He wore the best of his tall hats,
A coat with tails, and dove-grey spats,
And went on fishing, rain or shine,
With rod and reel and hook and line,

But never caught a thing, they say,
Until he tumbled in, one day
And there, as from the foam he rose,
A crab was clinging to his nose.

As Jane the housemaid said to cook,
"It really was (but please don't look)
A very different kind of hook."

And now, alas, when Dabbie tries
To prove a thing contrariwise,
And argue in his table-talk
That chalk is cheese and cheese is chalk,
For since they both are soft and white
To eat them both is a delight,
That wicked little Mrs. Dabbs
Just looks at him and murmurs "Crabs."

A SURPRISE FOR SUSAN

She was wide awake that evening.
   It was no use counting sheep,
So she slipped out of bed and looked through the window
   At a garden fast asleep.

There was one wee croak in the stillness
   From a lump on the fountain's rim,
Where a frog looked up at the evening star,
   And the star looked back at him.

There was one wee glimmer in the long grass
   Where a gold-green glowworm shone,
And just one light in the gardener's cottage,
   And suddenly that was gone.

There was nobody at all in the garden
   That Susan's eyes could see,
"We always keep our secrets,"
   Breathed the shivering aspen-tree.

Then the moon made a magic in the treetops,
   With her creeping, silvery spell;
And the whispering willow answered,
   "We keep our secret well."

Then Susan felt quite drowsy,
  And slipped back into bed.
"There'll be nobody at all in the garden
  Till I wake up," she said.

But when she woke next morning,
  There were daffodils laughing at the light,
And fifteen blossoms on the apple-tree,
  That had not been there last night!

UGLY LITTLE BELLA

As ugly little Bella took a very lonely walk
She met a handsome blackbird who didn't want to talk.
He stared at her. He glared at her. He screamed at her and
    fled;
And it so upset poor Bella that she went straight home to bed.

They sent for Doctor Rustikoff. He looked at Bella's tongue,
And wrote a grand prescription for an *aubade*[1] to be sung
By a choir of twelve green linnets, with a solo from a lark,
And a gurgle from a nightingale to soothe her through the
    dark.

They brought the grand prescription. The birds were in a cage,
The wild birds of April that had known the Golden Age,
And lifted up their soft throats through all the hours of light,
Till evening brought the nightingale for memory and the night.

But ugly little Bella simply laughed and cried and laughed,
Till Doctor Rustikoff declared she must be going daft.
Said she, "If you're a doctor, you're the daftest ever seen,
To put the singers in a cage when all the woods are green.

O, well I know there's healing where a happy linnet sings,
But (perhaps you haven't noticed) he has very lovely wings.
Open wide the window, please, and let them all go free,
And I hope they'll meet the blackbird who refused to talk with
    me."

[1] A dawn song, in case you wonder.

O, cruelly the sunlight through the open window shone
On ugly little Bella's face when all the birds were gone;
And Doctor Rustikoff declared she ought to have a nurse,
For she'd wrecked the grand prescription and would certainly
    grow worse.

Next day when ugly Bella walked alone in yonder wood,
And tried to hide her ugliness beneath a kind of hood,
The handsome blackbird fluted from an overhanging spray,
"It isn't any secret here, disguise it as you may!

Your hood can never hide it, I can read it in your eyes."
Sarcastical she thought it, talking so of her disguise.
Then he fluttered to her shoulder, fluting softly in her ear,
"We will keep your secret, Bella—but you're awful pretty,
    dear!"

Saint George he slew the dragon,
  But he didn't shout hurray.
He dumped it in the wagon
  Just to clear the mess away.

But the wagoner he sold it
  To a showman at the Fair,
And when Saint George was told it,
  He was almost in despair,

For the people crowded round it
  To admire its teeth and claws,
But Saint George he was an Englishman
  And did not like applause.

"The creechah weighed a ton at most,"
  He muttered through his vizahd.
"I do not feel inclined to boast
  About that puny lizahd."

Said rich Uncle Sam-u-el to little James his nephew
   (James was in a hospital, recovering from mumps):
"Here's a sweet surprise for you—I've brought you a canary
   To whistle in your window when you're feeling in the
      dumps."

But little James croaked eerily to rich Uncle Sam-u-el,
   (Talking isn't easy when your throat is full of lumps),
"I don't like canaries; I'd much prefer a cam-u-el),
   A tall live cam-u-el, with two large humps."

Said rich Uncle Sam-u-el, a-trying for to humor him,
   "The nurses and the doctors here are all off their chumps.[1]
They say there isn't room in this nice big hospital,
   Unless we find a cam-u-el that hasn't any humps."

Said little James his nephew, to rich Uncle Sam-u-el,
   "I don't ask for kangaroos, or anything that jumps.
I only want a cam-u-el, a nice large cam-u-el,
   A tall live cam-u-el with two large humps."

[1] English for nutty, like fruitcakes.

A CHILD'S VISION

Under the sweet peas I stood
And drew deep breaths. They smelt so good.
Then, with strange enchanted eyes,
I saw them change to butterflies.

Higher than the skylark sings
I saw their fluttering crimson wings
Leave their garden-trellis bare
And fly into the upper air.

Standing in an elfin trance
Through the clouds I saw them glance . . .
Then I stretched my hand up high
And touched them in the distant sky.

At once the coloured wings came back
From wandering in the Zodiac.
Under the sweet peas I stood
And drew deep breaths. They smelt so good.

BRIGHT MOUNTAINS

There were hundreds of snowy white mountains
    All sailing along in the sky;
And the sky was as blue as the Channel
    Where yachts like white blossoms went by,
When, over the lawn, hopped a red-breast,
    As proud as a toreador,
And cocked his bright eye at a worm-hole,
    Which proved it was going to pour!

For robin knows more about weather
    And worms than the gardeners do;
And he swallowed a little one, wriggling,
    And whistled his grace to the blue;
And the sun didn't turn into shadow;
    The warmth didn't turn into cold;
But out of the snowy white mountains
    Came flashes and splashes of gold.

And Nanny said "Rain! What a nuisance!"
    But Mummie said, "April! What fun!
Quick, Billikins! Put on your bunglings[1]
    And out on the grass for a run!"
Wet buttercups, out in the meadow!
    Wet crocuses under the trees!
And—trumpets of gold in the orchard—
    Wet daffodils, up to your knees!

[1] Bunglings, the nursery name for rubber boots.

And the ducks at the farm were all squattering
  And gobbling the squashy wet grass;
And I danced in a beautiful puddle
  That showed the whole sky like a glass.
I scattered the clouds as they floated;
  I broke up the sun on its track;
Then—*I watched, till the dark pool remembered;*
  And all the bright mountains came back.

JANE'S PAIN

Jane, Jane!
Oh, I know you've a pain,
But who has been robbing the larder again?

Who stole downstairs
After saying her prayers,
And ate three peaches and two large pears?

Does the pain suggest
A lump in your chest?
The wings of the chicken have both gone west!

The remains of the veal—
There, there! don't squeal!
I know what a sensitive child must feel.

The three soft roes
That your mother chose
For your grandfather's gums, what has happened to those?

Jane, Jane!
You've been at it again,
And I really do hope it's a *very* bad pain.

TIMMY AND HIS TUMMY

Said Timmy to his Mummie,
  "I could eat the *whole* of that.
If it wasn't for my tummy
  You could hardly call me fat."

Said his Mummie to her Timmy,
"When the cakes and buns appear
There's a busy '*Gimme, gimme!*'
In your dizzy Mummie's ear.

Your rotundity of tummy
    Only shows how it begins.
You will look extremely rummy
    When you've forty-seven chins!

Pray observe your Uncle Dennis,
    How he leaps across the lawn
When he takes a turn at tennis,
    Like a nimble-footed fawn.

He is satisfied with plenty,
    And he never asks for more.
That is why his waist is twenty
    And his chest is forty-four."

Then said Timmy to his Mummie,
    "Don't you think it might be best,
After mealtimes that my tummy
    Should be counted as my chest?"

A FRENCH LESSON

In France the fleecy muttons munch
    The thyme upon the hills,
And mooing beefs in meadows crunch
    The crisp young daffodils.

In France their very noses neigh,
    They use their grass for grace,
And even a modest nun will say
    Her figure is her face.

INDIAN TALLY

*This was a game described by a New England squirrel to two
little boys who got lost in the woods of Maine while they were
playing at Redskins. The squirrel talked to them while they
were asleep under a pine tree, and it sounded as if all the
Indian tribes at that time were friendly. Of course, being only
a squirrel, he may have been wrong, but he got the names of
the trees and shrubs right.*

This is the game called Injun Tally
Which used to be played in the Mohawk Valley,
In days when the world was not so round
An' its woods were the Red Man's huntin' ground;
Where a Redskin lad might lie in the sun
An' look at the sky when his work was done;
An' say to a drowsin' Sioux or Crow
*"How many scents of the wood d'you know?
Breathe through your nose an' shut your eyes,
An' say how many you reckernize."*
An' the Crow would answer, "My nose discerns
A balsam fir in the lake-side ferns;
An' a little beyond, if I'm not mistook,
A rough red spruce by a chucklin' brook;
An' I'm nigh sartin I can smell
Maple sap . . . an' a moose as well!"
Then the Mohawk lad would say, "That's four;
But *my* nose gives me fifty more.
I smell lindens, dizzy with bees,
An' bright witch-hazels round their knees.
I smell cedar, an' sweet gum,

Puckery crab, an' Canada plum;
Young birch-twigs that a deer has cropt;
Rosin of larch where a bough's bin lopt;
Locusts bitter where pods have burst;
An' sorrel, sour for the hunter's thirst."

Drowsily then the Sioux would say,
"Ten ain't much for a summer's day.
I can pick out, one by one,
All the trails where the chipmunks run.
I smell succory, timothy grass,
Red bark, slivers of sassafras,
Basswood honey, and tangled vine,
Heather that breathes like Frenchman's wine,

Musk that hides the field mouse track,
Mint that brings your memory back,
Balm of Gilead's teasin' scent,
An' hemlock boughs to straw your tent."
Then, gazin' queerly at the sky,
The Mohawk lad would make reply,
"Call it twelve. The game is done.
My nose beats your twelve with one.
I smell knots of black pitch-pine,
Oozin' tar an' turpentine,
Hickory trees where the squirrels play,
Bilberry, barberry, juniper, bay,
Wild black cherry an' linseed flax,
Wrinkled elder that blunts your axe,
Hackberry, blackberry, wild sweet briar,
An' blue wood-smoke from a red camp-fire,
Where you an' the Crow (if you want *your* share)
Will now, *at once*, with me repair;
For there, if this Mohawk nose ain't boastin',
I distinguish *turkey, roastin'*."

THE SKUNK

Jacko the Skunk, in black and white,
Walked up the road one summer night,
And there he met, in gold and green,
The biggest toad he'd ever seen.

Said Mr. Skunk to Mr. Toad,
"This is a strictly private road.
You need no sign-post, I suppose?"
"No," said the Toad, "I have my nose."

"Wazzat?" "Oh my! Gee whiz! Gee whiz!
A private road? It surely is.
Truer word was never said.
Phew!!" cried Mr. Toad—and fled.

THE MAGICIANS

"If I were the bluebird that fashioned the sky,"
    Said the little blue wizard to me,
With a flirt of his wings and a flash of his eye,
    As he perched in the crab apple tree,
"If I were the Master-Magician, I'd make
The Universe over again for our sake.

The world should be all under bluebird control,
    And boys should be just of a size
For me and my missus to swallow 'em whole
    Like spiders or honey-fed flies;
While earth should have nothing but trees on her breast,
Where bluebirds like me and my missus could nest."

"If I were the web-footed Wizard you mean,"
    Croaked a fat little bullfrog below,
"I should bubble and squeak in an oozier green
    Than aught in the world that we know;
While your twittering song would grow vital and harsh,
For I'd turn the whole universe into a marsh."

Oh, crimson as wine were the beautiful beads
    Of his eyes, as he stared at the West,
And croaked, "I'd have nothing but puddles and reeds!
    I don't see the use of a nest!
I'd have millions of gnats" (his eyes blackened like blood),
"And legions of wives all asprawl in the mud—"

"If I were the mouse that created us all,"
  A squeak in the wainscot began,
"The moon that goes rolling about like a ball,
  Would be made on a far better plan.
It's really absurd; it provokes me to mirth,
That the moon should be cheese while the mice are on earth."

"If I were the Queen of the Universe," purred
  The little black witch with the claws,
"How the mouse and the frog and the mesmerized bird
  Would love the red yawn of my jaws!
How the mouldy old houses would rustle with rats,
If the world were arranged for the comfort of cats!

How men, at one twitch of my whiskers, would fly
    To fetch me my milk in a bowl;
And how, at one wink of my wicked green eye,
    They would feed me on salmon and sole;
How sweetly my kittens would sleep overhead,
In the very best sheets of the very best bed."

"If I could remodel the universe," cried
    The man on the tub to the crowd.
"We've heard the suggestion before," they replied,
    And they melted away like a cloud.
For they thought it might lead to some dreadful mistakes
If he made the world over again for their sakes.

"It is better," they growled, "that to each should be given
    His own bit of bliss, if you please,
Than that earth should be turned into somebody's heaven,
    Which might be a marsh or a cheese.
As the Sage told the onions, 'We're all of some use,
If it's only for stuffing the tail of a goose.'"

THE MILKMAN

The Milkman brings the milk in bottles;
His fields are fenced around with wattles.[1]
I don't think he has much to hide,
But I should like to look inside.

His name is Mr. Pump, it's true,
But that's a thing he would not do.
His milk and cream are quite delicious.
It's just his ways that are suspicious.

[1] A high wooden fence that you can't see through.

HENRY FAIRCHILD

What shall we do with Henry Fairchild?
What *shall* we do with Henry Fairchild?
What *Can* we do with Henry Fairchild,
    At breakfast-time in the morning?

He's so refeened that he talks with a mew,
And offers you his paw saying "How-d'ye-do?
I've met the Duke of Dorking, but I can't remember *you*."
    At breakfast-time in the morning.

Of course his Aunt Jemima thinks he's terribly polite,
For the Duke of Dorking told him his Aunt was always right,
So that even when she scolds him he can only answer "Quite,"
    At breakfast-time in the morning.

But he'll seize your pat of butter with a jocular "Ha-ha!
I can do with all of this, but how delightful of you. Ta!
I shall tell the Duke of Dorking what a jolly chap you are."
    At breakfast-time in the morning.

If you tell him of a story that you think is really great,
He will eye his little wristwatch, "It's getting late;
And don't you think, old fellow, you are rahther out-of-date?"
    At breakfast-time in the morning.

Of course he's only echoing what polly parrot said,
When he listened at the keyhole and she thought he was in bed;
So the only cure for Henry is to hit him on the head,
    At breakfast-time in the morning.

What shall we do with Henry Fairchild?
What *shall* we do with Henry Fairchild?
What *Can* be Done with Henry Fairchild,
    At breakfast-time in the morning?

Hit him on the head with the works of Shakespeare.
He says they were written by Nicholas Breakspeare,
So hit him on the head with the works of Shakespeare,
    At breakfast-time in the morning.

IT WASN'T MY FAULT

"It wasn't my fault," said the rough old Skye,
   "It wasn't my fault at all;
But she arched her back as I passed her by,
   And she sprang to the top of the wall.

'That's fun,' I thought, and all that I said
   Was a single approving 'woof,'
And she jumped right over the potting shed,
   And dropped on the hen-house roof;

And the hens all flapped their wings and ran
   On their stiff little stick-like legs;
And I know that it quite upset their plan
   Of laying a few more eggs.

O, her eyes were green and her coat was black,
   And I'm only an old grey Skye,
But I really don't think she should arch her back
   When a gentleman passes by."

A CHILD'S GALLOP

(The refrain in the following poem is a child's version of an old nursery song in the patois of Languedoc.)

Where the great hills meet the sky,
Where the wheeling plovers cry,
Where the foxglove belfries burn
Crimson over seas of fern—
Head uplifted, face alight,
Eyes and stirrups glittering bright,
Rides my little girl of girls
With a tempest in her curls;
Heels thrust down, and mouth a rose,
Hear her singing as she goes:

Allons! Allons, chivalet!
À la fièro dal Coulet,
Porterai un gros couteau!
Allons, allons, moun chivau!

See, her charger turns again,
Flowing tail and tossing mane,
Like a wave with stormy crest,
And a glory in its breast,
Knowing that an elf of nine
Rules it now by right divine.
Hear the warrior hoof-beats come,
Clattering like a kettle-drum!
Hear her singing, low and loud,
To the skylark and the cloud:

Allons! Allons, moun chivau,
À la guerro je m'en vau!
Pat-a-trica, pat-a-tra!
La nous ferons tout tramblà!

BETSY JANE'S SIXTH BIRTHDAY

"I should like to buy you a birthday present," said Billy to
    Betsy Jane,
"I should like to buy you a motorcar, a ship and a railway train.
I should like to buy you a rose-red ribbon to stick in your hair
    or hat;
But I've only a penny left in my purse, and I can't buy much
    for that."

"But that's all right," said Betsy Jane. "In mine, there's a shil-
    ling or two.
I think you had better take *my* purse. I should *like* a present
    from *you*."
So putting their golden heads together it all came right as rain;
And the happiest eyes in the world that day were the eyes of
    Betsy Jane.

THE SKYLARK'S WEDDING

When dawn made a beautiful rose of the dark,
And before the old watch-dog could wake up and bark,
The woodpecker married a mad little lark,
 Singing, tirrily, tirrily, over the clouds,
  How jimpsome it is in the sky!

"We have nothing for supper," the woodpecker said;
When up buzzed a bee, with a loaf on his head,
Ay, a crusty brown loaf of the very best bread,
 Singing tirrily, tirrily, clover and meadow-sweet,
  Never say death till you die!

"Now we've plenty of bread; but, alas and alack,
Not a flagon of wine or a pottle of sack."
Then up ran an ant with a butt on his back,
 Singing, I am the ant that was never a sluggard,
  Ask me not wherefore or why!

"We have wine, we have bread," said those lovers in grief;
"But the joint?"—on that instant and light as a leaf,
Came a butterfly bearing a brisket of beef,
 With a twinkle and wink of his beautiful tortoiseshell
  Wings that went fluttering by.

"Now we've beef, wine and bread, but the fruit's all to seek,
And to grow a new orchard would take a whole week!"
Then a pigeon flew down with ripe figs in his beak,
 With a roucoulou, roucoulou, roucoulou, roucoulou,
  Iris and dewy black eye.

"Fruit and meat, wine and bread, but no dancers to dance!"
Then they looked and they stared and beheld in a trance,
All the grasshoppers round them beginning to prance,
    With a tirrily, rumble, and roucoulou, roucoulou,
        Oh, how could they hop it so high.

"That's dancers in plenty, but music? Where's that?"
"Oh, I'll scrape the cat-gut if you'll bell the cat,"
Said the bridegroom. "We've only to laugh and grow fat!"
    With a tirrily, mew-mew, rumble and roucoulou
        Umps, what a fiddler am I!

The cat, in the catmint, she heard where she lay.
She crept an inch nearer, to hear the lad play,
Then the fiddle squeaked, once, and she pounced on her prey,
    Singing rumble and grumble, mew-mew and roucoulou,
        Lawks! how the feathers did fly!

THE PAINT-BOX

At breakfast, on my birthday, came a gift from Aunt Matilda—
    A paint-box, with the palette and the brushes all complete.
She was *sure* I was an artist. She had *seen* me drawing angels
    (They were meant for fan-tailed pigeons) and she called
      them *"very* sweet."

She had told me of another boy (I think his name was Jotto)
    Who did some things called frescoes. They were paintings
      on a wall.
It sounded most attractive. I thought I'd like to try it,
    And what could be more helpful than to decorate the hall,

Or, better still, the dining room. It hadn't any pictures.
    The walls were what Mama had called "a quiet duck-egg
      blue."
Of course I wouldn't spoil them; but I thought, perhaps, like
      Jotto,
    I could warm them up a little with a jolly face or two.

Snouts and curly tails were easy, so I painted lots of piglets
    Dancing round a burly bulldog who was smoking a cigar.
He was wearing striped pyjamas and a hat that didn't fit him,
    Just like Mr. Winston Churchill. This I thought would please
      Papa.

Then I did some spotted horses. Though their legs were
    knobbly-wobbly,
    They had noble Roman noses. After that I drew a Saint
Looking cross-eyed at a demon who had shot him in the giz-
    zard
    With that angel-feathered arrow Brother Jotto used to paint.

I had done the gory crimson just as Jane the housemaid
    entered,
    And goggled at me in a way that made my tonsils creep.
"*Goolawk!*" she squawked, "I'm going to faint!" I answered,
    "It's a fresco."
    "*Goolawk!*" she squawked, "It's nightmares an' I'm walking
    in my sleep."

They sent the gorgeous paint-box back with love to Aunt
    Matilda.
    They said I was a "moddun" and I couldn't need it less;
But even from my bedroom I could hear the guests at dinner
    Saying Jotto's little party was a really huge success.

PORPOISES

The porpoises at dinner time were rolling through the bay,
All a-following their leader in a very pleasant way,
Rising up and reeling under with an oily kind of ease,
And a-turning topsy-turvy through the laughter of the seas.

I wondered, as I watched them, if they did it all for fun,
And the answer flashed to meet me, bright as rain-drops in
the sun.
Twenty thousand little fishes that I hadn't seen before,
Leapt in twenty thousand splashes from the shallows to the
shore.

Little sprats with frightened faces, leaping madly for the land,
Where they kickled it in silver, on the wet and shining sand.
"Whales," they gasped, "may think it funny. No one swallows
whales alive!
Little fishes look for tree-tops when the porpoises arrive."

THE UNCHANGING SONG

The speckled thrush of Spring
   Hides in the hawthorn snow,
And wakes me with the song he used to sing
   Hundreds of years ago.

Proud knights in armour heard,
   And paused upon their way,
To catch the very notes that one dear bird
   Repeats for me today.

CHERRIES—OR BLACKBIRDS

With blossom, first, the boughs grew white,
  Then black with cherry on cherry,
Then, feasting to their heart's delight,
  A flock of birds made merry.
They did so rustle from tree to tree
  And merrily pick their own,
There wasn't a cherry for you or me
  When those black thieves had flown.

Yet one sweet thief at the edge of the wood
  So lifted his throat and sang
How cherries were ripe and juicy and good,
  That all the green wood rang.
O who could choose between birds and berries?
  I'm sure that riddle is wrong
For if he'd offered me two ripe cherries,
  I'd've joined that rogue in the song.

GOOD-NIGHT

The black rooks in the sunset light
    Are cawing overhead.
With every caw they say good-night,
    It's time I went to bed.

Good-night! I've had a heavenly day,
    And now, before I go,
The thank you that I want to say
    Is very small, I know.

A wren, and lots of other birds,
    Are saying it out there,
But not, of course, the usual words
    That Mum and Daddy hear.

But thank you, thank you, all the same,
    For all the fun I've found
With all the creatures, wild and tame,
    That haunt our hunting ground,

The squirrel and the velvet mole,
    And best, I think, of all,
The prickly hedgehog that can roll
    His quills into a ball.

Thank you for every blundering bee
   That tastes the honeyed thyme,
For eggs, and buttered toast at tea,
   And funny bits of rhyme,

For happy faces all a-glow
   To hear an evening tale,
Of great adventures long ago
   On seas that none can sail.

It's time to go. The drowsy rooks
   Have lost the sunset light.
Thank you for birds, and flowers, and books.
   O happy world, Good-Night.

A SLUMBER SONG

Sandman's coming—childhood echoes
   All that eld may know—
Soft and grey the streams of slumber
   Through his fingers flow.
Nearer now his quiet footsteps
   Creep and creep and creep.
Sandman's coming. Little cowboy,
   Tuck you up and sleep.

Sandman's coming—rose and opal
   Tinge the glimmering west.
Earth is hushed. The solemn ocean
   Rocks the ship to rest.
Cry of watchman shall not wake you
   On that boundless deep.
Sandman's coming. Little sailor,
   Tuck you up and sleep.

Sandman's coming through the ages,
   Pouring darker streams,
Drowning wars and broken kingdoms
   In his drift of dreams.
Now the unremembering shepherds
   Nod beside their sheep.
Sandman's coming. Little soldier,
   Tuck you up and sleep.

Darker grows the night and darker,
  And poor Tom's a-cold
Eld that cannot solve the riddle
  Leaves the tale untold.
He who ends the tale hereafter
  Endless watch must keep.
Sandman ends the endless ages.
  Tuck you up and sleep.